FRED BASSET YEARBOOK 2013

Summersdale Publishers Ltd
46 West Street
Chichester
West Sussex
PO19 1RP
UK

www.summersdale.com

Printed and bound in the Czech Republic

Drawings by Michael Martin

ISBN: 978-1-84953-310-2

Substantial discounts on bulk quantities of Summersdale books are available to corporations, professional associations and other organisations.
For details contact Summersdale Publishers by telephone: +44 (0) 1243 771107, fax: +44 (0) 1243 786300 or email: nicky@summersdale.com.

WHAT DO YOU WANT, FRED?

And there's me thinking I was stating the obvious!

Just a frozen puddle to some...

...but a skating rink to Yorky!

...AND FIRST PRIZE GOES TO JOHNNY JONES!

A spot of nepotism if you ask me!

THANK YOU, AUNTIE JOAN!

PAINTING COMPETITION

Yes, Jock— Very impressive. No, we don't want to see your backward somersault AGAIN, thankyou—

Yorky!

Don't encourage him!

Yip Yip Yip Yip Yip Yip Yip

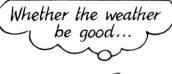

A total eclipse!

Otherwise known as Big Bruce!

WELL, DO YOU WANT TO PLAY OR NOT?!

I think we may have met our match, lads!

UM...?

Don't worry, Jock — Your secret's safe with me!

HAVE YOU BEEN DIGGING IN MY ROSE BED, FRED?!

No!

Oh, hang on a moment...

Yes!

I had a slight memory lapse!

FRED SEEMS TO BE ENJOYING HIMSELF —

I make a fine figurehead!

I don't know why I bother chasing the little perishers—

I never catch any!

They always seem to get off to a flying start!

I make an ideal paperweight!

Come back, you little rascal!

Gotcha!

A right little escapologist, aren't we?!

If there's one thing that's sure to drive me round the bend —

It's the Grosvenor Avenue Gang!

COME ON FRED — UP AND OVER!

Up and over?!

If it's all the same to you...

I prefer *down and under!*